Silver Sails

A Beka Book® Reading Program

Laurel Hicks, *Editor*
Illustrated by **Mike Davis**

A Beka Book®
A MINISTRY OF
PENSACOLA CHRISTIAN COLLEGE
PENSACOLA, FLORIDA 32523-9160

Acknowledgment

Ellen C. Babbitt, *The Jatakas: Tales of India,* ©1912, pp. 30–33, 58–62. Reprinted by permission of Prentice Hall, Englewood Cliffs, New Jersey.

1986 Edition

Silver Sails

Guide to Story Themes

A Beka Book® Reading Program

Handbook for Reading (grades 1–3)
Primary Bible Reader (grades 1–3)
Read & Think Skill Sheets (grades 4–6)

1 Fun with Pets
Tiptoes
Stepping Stones
Secrets and Surprises
The Bridge Book
Open Windows
Kind and Brave
Aesop's Fables
Strong and True

2 Story Tree
Treasure Chest
Hidden Treasure
No Longer a Nobody
Paths of Gold
New Reader 2
All Things—Even Frisky
Silver Sails
Growing Up Where
Jesus Lived
All Kinds of Animals

3 Footprints
Crossroads
Paths to Follow
Pilgrim Boy
Secret in the Maple Tree
Better Bridges
Golden Windows
Pilgrim's Progress

4 Song of the Brook
Frontiers to Explore
Liberty Tree
Flags Unfurled
Enchanted Isles

5 Noah Webster: A Man Who
Loved Words
Widening Horizons
Of America 1
Adventures in Nature
(Speed and Comprehension)

6 Rosa
Adventure Lands
Of America 2
Adventures in Greatness
(Speed and Comprehension)

Introduction

Children are eagerly searching for a workable sense of values. They need to see in the lives of great people, common people, and children like themselves, the unchanging values of the ages lived out. They need reading material that will give them ideals to reach for and examples to follow.

The stories in this reader have been selected from the readers of America's past and have been edited, modernized, and classroom-tested for student appeal and readability. This reader will introduce to children not only what is excellent in itself, but what their parents and grandparents have read before them—stories so good that they will never become old and stories that impart moral values.

These values are taught throughout the book—honesty, integrity, courage, faith, kindness, forgiveness, industry, unselfishness, patriotism, and respect for authority.

Thought questions at the end of the stories greatly aid in the understanding and appreciation of the selections.

Contents

William Tell

Very far from here, on the other side of the sea, there is a beautiful country called Switzerland. In that country there are many high mountains, with green valleys and pretty lakes. And there are towns and pleasant country homes where many free and happy people live.

But the people of Switzerland were not always free and happy. A long time ago, an army of strangers crossed the mountains, came down into the valleys, and tried to rob the Swiss of all that they had.

There were some brave men among the Swiss, and these fought for their country and their homes as long as they could. But they were beaten in every battle. The strangers took their houses, their fields, and their cattle, and left them almost nothing to call their own.

One of the strangers, whose name was

Gessler, became the ruler of the Swiss. He was very cruel and treated them as slaves.

Among the mountains, there lived a brave huntsman called William Tell. There was no one in all the world who could shoot with a bow and arrows as well as he. Tell hated the cruel Gessler and the strangers that had come with him into Switzerland, and he longed for the day to come when they could be driven out of the land.

One day Gessler had a tall pole put up in the public square. On the top of the pole his own hat was hung. Then he gave orders that every man who passed by the square should bow to this hat. There was one who would not do this. That man was William Tell.

When Gessler heard that Tell had passed the pole and had not bowed to the hat on top of it, he was glad. Why? He now had a good excuse for putting Tell in prison. For he was afraid of the huntsman, and wanted very much to put him where he could do no harm.

William Tell was thrown into prison and kept there for a long time. Gessler did not want him to be free again. A little boy of Tell's was also put into prison, for, like his father, he would not bow to Gessler's hat.

One day Gessler thought of a cruel plan. He ordered Tell to be brought before him.

"I hear," he said, "that you can shoot well with a bow and arrow."

Tell answered, "If I had my bow in my hand, I might show you."

"That is just what I want you to do," said Gessler; "and that is what you shall do. Tomorrow, your son shall stand at one side of the public square, with an apple on his head. You shall stand at the other side and shoot the apple with an arrow."

"You do not mean it," said Tell.

"I do mean it," said Gessler. "If you will not do it, your son shall be killed before your eyes. One of my men shall shoot him with an arrow."

Tell begged Gessler not to make him do this. "You want me to kill my boy," he said.

"No," said Gessler, "I want you to shoot the apple, and if you do not hit it, both you and your boy shall die."

"And what if I do hit it?" asked Tell.

"Then both of you shall go free," said Gessler. So at last Tell said he would try.

The next day the little boy was made to stand at one side of the public square with a small apple on his head. "I am not afraid, Father," he said. "I know you will hit it."

William Tell, with his bow and arrow, stood at the other side of the square. "It is a long way to shoot," he said, "and the sun shines in my eyes."

"Don't say a word," said Gessler.

Tell lifted his strong bow and drew the arrow back. There was not another man in Switzerland who could bend that bow.

"You have given me a crooked arrow," he said. "Let me have a straight one."

"Don't say a word," said Gessler. "Shoot!"

Tell raised the bow again. Then, twang! The arrow went flying through the air. There was a great shout from the people. What did it mean?

8

Tell had turned his face. He would not look, for he was afraid that he had shot his child. Then he felt a little arm around his neck. "Father, I am safe! The arrow went right through the center of the apple!"

That was why the people shouted. Even Gessler's men were glad. But Gessler was angry. He would have broken his word, and sent Tell back to prison, if he had dared.

But he saw that Tell had more friends than he.

"You may go free, now," he said. "But do not come in my way again."

William Tell and his child went back to their home among the mountains, and the good wishes of all the people went with them. Soon after this, the Swiss people drove the army of strangers back across the mountains, and their country was free again.

Can You Tell?

1. What things show that William Tell was brave and kind?
2. What things show that Tell's little boy was brave and obedient?

Androclus and the Lion

Once there lived in the city of Rome a man whose name was Androclus. He was tall and fair and strong, but he was a slave. He had to work day and night for his master. He had nothing that he could call his own.

One day his master beat him. "Why should I live in this way?" said Androclus. "It would be better to die." That night he ran away. He hid himself in the woods, and

Words to Watch For

wounded   chariot   arena

lived on berries and roots for many days.

But at last he could not find anything to eat. He went into a little cave and lay down on the ground. He had not had food for three days. He thought he would die.

As Androclus was lying in the cave, he heard a noise at the door. He looked up and saw a lion coming in. "The beast will kill me," he thought, and he lay very still.

But the lion was in trouble. It held up one of its paws and roared. Then it looked at Androclus as if to say, "I want help." Androclus got up. He was so weak that it was hard for him to walk. He went to the lion and looked at its paw. The big beast did not try to hurt him.

Androclus saw that there was a long, sharp thorn in its paw; it must have stepped on the thorn when it was coming through the woods. The lion seemed to know that it had found a friend. It held up its paw and sat quite still while the man looked at it.

Then with great care Androclus pulled the thorn out. He washed the wounded paw in cold water and bound it up with a piece of cloth which he tore from his coat.

The lion licked his hand and seemed to be very glad. It ran about him like a playful dog. Then it went out of the cave, and soon came back with part of a deer which it had killed.

Androclus gathered some leaves and sticks and built a fire. Soon he had a better dinner than he had eaten for many a day. While he was eating, the lion sat close by and looked at him as if it were much pleased.

When night came the lion lay down in a corner of the cave to sleep, and Androclus lay down by its side.

And so the two lived together in the cave in the woods for a long time. Every day the lion brought food to Androclus; and every night they slept together, like two brothers, on a bed of leaves in the little cave.

One day the lion did not come home from hunting, and that night Androclus slept alone in the cave. The next morning he went out to look for his friend.

He had not gone far when he heard a noise among the leaves behind him. He looked around and saw some soldiers close upon him. The soldiers knew him.

"Androclus!" they said. "We have been looking for you for a long time. Your master wants you, and you must go with us."

What could Androclus do? There were ten soldiers, and he had no one to help him. Where was his good friend, the lion?

The soldiers made him go back to the city with them, and his master had him put in prison. "We shall see if you run away from us again," said his master. Androclus felt now that there was no more hope.

Some time after that, there was a great holiday in Rome. There were to be all kinds of games in the afternoon. There were to be foot races and chariot races; and, at the last, there was to be a fight between a man and a fierce and hungry lion.

But who was to fight the lion? Some man would be taken from prison and placed where the lion would come upon him. Whether the man fought or not, the lion would be sure to eat him up.

The people of Rome were not Christians, and they liked to see all this. They liked to see the poor man's fright. They liked to see the fierce beast jump upon him. But there were many men in the prison. Which one of them should be given to the lion?

"There is my slave," said the master of Androclus. "He is of no use to me. He runs away and will not work. Let him fight the lion. He is strong and brave, and it will be good sport to see the beast eat him up."

"So it will," said the others. "He is the very man." And so Androclus was taken out of prison to be eaten by the lion.

Androclus was led out and left alone in the open space called the arena. There was no way for him to get out. He had only his hands to fight with. There was no one to help him.

On high seats around the arena sat the fine people of Rome, who had come out to see the games of the day. At one side of the arena were cages full of wild beasts.

And now the door of one of these cages was opened. A lion jumped out. It looked around. It saw Androclus and ran toward him. All the people thought that it would kill Androclus at once.

But when it came closer to him, it stopped. Then it ran to him as if it were glad to see him. It lay down on the ground before him. It licked his hands and face.

Androclus took the lion's paw in his hands; then he put his arms around its neck. He had found his old friend that had lived with him in the little cave!

The people who were looking on did not know what to think. They all stood up in wonder. They called out to Androclus and asked him why it was that he and the lion were friends. Then Androclus told them all about it.

The people were very much pleased. "Let them both live!" they all cried. "Let them both go free!" And so, while everybody shouted and was glad, Androclus led the lion out of the arena. He had no master now. He was a free man.

For many years after that, he and his lion lived together in a house in the city of Rome. And everybody said, "See how much they are like two brothers!"

Do You Remember?

1. What city was Androclus from?
2. How did Androclus and the lion become friends?
3. Why was Androclus put into the arena?
4. Why were the people pleased?

Write a Story

Write a story about two friends helping each other. The friends can be either animals or people.

How the Sea Became Salt

Here is an old story about how the sea became salt. It is not a true story, but it is fun to read.

Once upon a time there were two brothers. One was very selfish and wanted to have everything for himself. The other was kind and gentle and always ready to do what he could to help others.

When they grew to be men, the selfish brother was rich and had a beautiful mansion and much property.

The gentle brother was a poor man. He lived in a small house and worked faithfully every day. Still, he was happier than his rich brother, for he always tried to do right.

Words to Watch For

mansion	property	difficult
	journey	desired

One winter, the poor brother became very ill. He could not do any work, and so there was no money in the house.

It was a difficult winter for him and his wife. They did not have enough food to eat, and they went cold because they could not buy wood to burn.

The poor brother finally grew better,

but he was still very weak and not able to work.

It was Christmas time. The poor brother did not have anything in his house for Christmas dinner. He and his wife were very hungry.

"I will go and ask my brother to give us something to eat," said he.

When the rich brother saw him at his door, he was angry.

He did not want to give him anything, but it was Christmas time. At that time everyone gives presents, so he did not like to say "no."

He threw a ham at his brother and said, "Take that, and go away."

The poor brother took the ham under his arm and started on his journey home. He felt very sad.

He traveled along slowly, with the ham under his arm. Soon he came to a forest where he saw an old man chopping wood.

"Good evening," said the old man.

"Good evening," said the poor brother.

"What a fine ham you have," said the old man. "Where did you get it?"

Then the poor brother told him all about his rich brother and the gift of the ham.

"It is fortunate that you met me," said the old man. "Take the ham to the land where the dwarves live. Then you will become very rich. The dwarves like ham very much, but they do not have it where they live."

"Where is the land of the dwarves?" asked the poor brother.

"I will tell you," said the old man. "Do you see that large oak tree?"

"Yes," said the brother.

"There is a stone under that tree; under that stone is a door. Open the door and it will let you into the land of the dwarves.

"Do not sell the ham to the dwarves

for money," said the old man. "Tell them that they must give you the old handmill that hangs behind the door. When you get this handmill, bring it to me, and I will show you how to use it."

The poor brother thanked the old man, and traveled on.

He found the stone under the tree, and under the stone he spied the door. He opened this door and went on until he came to the land of the dwarves.

There he saw funny little men; they smelled the ham, and came running to him as fast as they could.

"Please sell us some ham!" they cried. "Sell us some ham!"

They tried to get close to the poor brother; they pushed and crowded each other away.

"Here is money," they cried. "Give us the ham!"

"I do not want any money," said the poor brother. "I want the old handmill that hangs behind the door."

The dwarves did not wish to sell the handmill, for it was very useful to them. They had only to turn it, and out would come whatever they wished for. The only thing that it would not grind for them was ham.

"Give him the mill," said the king of the dwarves. "He will not know how to use it."

They did so. The poor brother then gave them the ham and went away with the handmill. He soon found the old man in the forest, and from him he learned how to use the mill.

Then he went home.

His wife was glad to see him, for he had been gone all day. She was hungry, for she had not had any dinner. She was cold, for there was no fire.

"What did your rich brother give you?" she asked.

"A ham," said the poor brother.

"Where is it?" asked his wife.

"I sold it to the dwarves."

"What did you get for it?"

"I got this old handmill," said the poor brother.

His wife was so cold and hungry that she began to cry. "Why did you not keep the ham?"

The poor brother put his handmill on the table and began to grind it.

"Grind a good dinner! Grind a good dinner!" he called out to the mill.

Out of the mill came a fine dinner. There were so many good things that the man and his wife could not eat them all.

"Grind a fire! Grind a fire!" said the poor brother. Then he turned the mill, and out came a warm fire.

"Grind a table! Grind a tablecloth! Grind

some spoons! Grind some forks! Grind some knives! Grind some dishes!"

Out of the mill came everything he asked for.

"Grind a new house!" said the brother.

Out of the mill came a beautiful new house.

All that the man and his wife had to do now was to wish for something and turn the mill, and out came what they wished for.

When they had everything that they desired for themselves, they told the mill to grind for other poor people.

It ground out food for the hungry people. If they needed clothes, the mill ground some for them.

The good mill worked all day. It ground fire and lights and food and clothes and shoes and stockings for those who needed them.

When the next Christmas Day came, the kind brother said to his wife, "Let us have a great feast. Then we will invite all the poor people in the country to come and have a fine dinner."

"Yes, we will," said his wife.

So the mill ground a fine dinner for them.

They sent for all the poor people. There was plenty for them all. How happy everyone was!

But there was one bad man at the feast. He was not a poor man, but he wanted to see the mill.

"I wish I had that mill," said he. "I would make it grind salt. Then I would sell the salt and become very rich."

He gave some money to one of the servants. "Steal that mill for me," he said. This was a bad servant, so he stole the mill and gave it to the man, who took it out on the sea in a ship.

"Grind salt!" said he to the mill.

Then it began to grind salt. It ground and ground until the ship was full of salt.

But the man did not know how to make it stop grinding salt. In vain he cried out, "Enough! Enough! We have enough salt!" The mill turned faster than ever. The salt made the ship so heavy that it sank to the bottom of the sea.

Some people say that the mill is down at the bottom of the sea now, still grinding salt, and that is why the sea water is salty.

White Butterflies

Fly, white butterflies, out to sea,
Frail, pale wings for the wind to try,
Small white wings that we scarce can see,
      Fly!
Some fly light as a laugh of glee,
Some fly soft as a long, low sigh;
All to the haven where each would be,
      Fly!

—*Algernon Charles Swinburne*

A Story
of George Washington

When George Washington was a boy, all this country was ruled by the king of England. Most of the people had come from England or were the children of Englishmen.

The king thought that it was a wise thing to make the people send to his own country for most of their clothes and tools. He would not let them have great shops or

Words to Watch For

plantation   distant   Virginia

mills in which to make things for themselves.

He thought that in this way he would bring much trade into England, and the English merchants would grow very rich.

There were but few towns in all the land. Most of these were near the seashore and quite small. Nearly all the people lived on farms or on great plantations,—sometimes near the bank of a river, and sometimes in the midst of the thick woods.

It was on one of these plantations, in that part of our country called Virginia, that George Washington lived when he was a boy.

On one side of this plantation there was a river that was broad and deep. Every summer a ship came sailing up the stream, and anchored a little way from the shore.

This ship had come from distant England, and it brought many beautiful things.

It brought fine dresses and bonnets for

George's mother and sisters, and sometimes it brought horses and wagons and plows to be used on the plantation.

When everything for the plantation had been brought to the shore, the ship would sail away. It would sail up the river, to stop at other places where goods had been ordered.

In a few weeks, it would come back and anchor again in the same spot. This time it would have nothing to leave. It came to take on the tobacco that had been raised on the plantation. The tobacco was to be carried to England to pay for the goods that had been bought.

George Washington had seen this ship come and go every summer since he could remember. He thought what a fine thing it must be to sail across the wide sea to the strange lands and wonderful cities that lie on the other side!

When he was about fourteen years old,

he began to think that a sailor's life would be more pleasant than that of a farmer on a lonely Virginia plantation.

His brothers also thought it might be best for him to go to sea; for George would not be a common sailor very long. He would soon be the captain of a ship.

So everything was made ready, and the captain of one of the king's ships said that he would take George with him.

The day came that was set for him to sail. All of George's friends were there to tell him good-by and see him start. The ship was waiting in the river.

The boat had come to take him on board. George felt very proud to think that he was going to be one of the king's sailors.

The little box that held his clothes had been carried down to the shore. The men were about to lift it into the boat.

George stood at the door. His heart was

sad at the thought of leaving home. "Good-by, Mother!" he said. He saw the tears in her eyes; he saw them running down her cheeks; he knew she did not want him to go.

He could not bear to see her distress. What if she should never be happy again? What if this should break her heart?

He turned to the servant boy who was waiting. "Run down to the landing, Bobby," he said, "and tell them not to put the box on board. Tell them that I am not going to sail in the ship."

Then he said, "Mother, I will stay with you and try to make you happy."

"George," said his mother, "there is a blessing promised to the child who honors his father and mother; I am sure this blessing will be yours."

The Bible Says

' Honor thy father and thy mother: that thy days be long upon the land which the Lord thy God thee."

—Exodus 20:12

Jesus Feeds
Five Thousand People

Jesus and his disciples wanted to be alone. They wanted to talk together and rest for a while. So they got into a boat and sailed across the sea of Galilee to a quiet place.

But the people loved Jesus. They wanted to be near him, too. When they saw him leaving, they followed after him, so that a great crowd of men and women and little children came to the place where he went.

Jesus did not send the people away; He was very kind to them. He taught them many things about God and about heaven, and He healed many persons who were sick. When it began to get dark, the disciples came to Jesus. "Send the people away,"

Words To Watch For

disciples   amazed   impossible

35

they said, "that they may go into the country round about, and into the villages, and buy themselves bread: for they have nothing to eat."

Jesus did not want to send the people away. They had come to Him for help, and He wanted to help them.

"Give ye them to eat," He said to the disciples.

The disciples were amazed. How could they feed so many people? It seemed impossible.

"How many loaves have ye?" said Jesus. "Go and see."

Andrew, one of the disciples, said, "There is a lad here, which hath five barley loaves, and two small fishes, but what are they among so many?"

Five little buns and two small fish! How could that ever feed five thousand people? What could Jesus do with one small lunch from one small boy? Everyone watched to see what would happen.

Jesus told the disciples to make all the people sit down in rows on the green grass. Taking the loaves of bread and the fish in His hand, He looked up to the sky and thanked God for them. Then Jesus broke the bread and the fish in pieces and gave the pieces to the disciples. The disciples went out and gave the food to the people.

As the disciples obeyed Jesus, a wonderful thing began to happen. As soon as they gave a piece of food to a person, another piece came. And so the pieces of bread and fish kept on coming, until all the men, women, and little children who were gathered together there had as much as they wanted to eat.

After everyone had had a good lunch, Jesus said to the disciples, "Gather up the fragments that remain, that nothing be lost."

The disciples picked up enough leftovers

from that little lunch to fill twelve large baskets!

It was Jesus who made the bread and fish keep on coming until all the people had had enough. This was a miracle—something that only God can do. Jesus could do miracles, for Jesus is God.

Jesus could give food to the hungry people. But He can do something better than that. He can feed our hungry hearts. He can make us happy and help us to do the things that He wants us to do. He can be "the Bread of Life" to us, if we will only trust Him.

The Bible Says

"And Jesus said unto them, I am the bread of life: he that cometh to me shall never hunger; and he that believeth on me shall never thirst."

—*John 6:35*

The Quarrel
of the Quails

Once upon a time many quails lived together in a forest. The wisest of them all was their leader.

A man lived near the forest and earned his living by catching quails and selling them. Day after day he listened to the note of the leader calling the quails. By and by this man, the fowler, was able to call the quails together. Hearing the note, the quails thought it was their leader who called.

When they were crowded together, the fowler threw his net over them, and off he went into the town, where he soon sold all the quails that he had caught.

The wise leader saw the plan of the fowler for catching the quails. He called the birds to him and said, "This fowler is carrying away so many of us, we must put a stop to it. I have thought of a plan; it is this: The next time the fowler throws a net over you, each of you must put your head through one of the little holes in the net. Then all of you together must fly away to the nearest thorn bush and free yourselves."

The quails said that was a very good plan and they would try it the next time the fowler threw the net over them.

The very next day the fowler came and called them together. Then he threw the net over them. The quails lifted the net and flew away with it to the nearest thorn bush, where they left it. They flew back to their leader to tell him how well his plan had worked.

The fowler was busy until evening getting his net off the thorns, and he went home empty-handed. The next day the same thing happened, and the next. His wife was angry because he did not bring home any money, but the fowler said, "The fact is those quails are working together now. The moment my net is over them, off they fly with it, leaving it on a thorn bush. As soon as the quails begin to quarrel, I shall be able to catch them."

Not long after this, one of the quails in alighting on their feeding ground, stepped by accident on another's head. "Who stepped on my head?" angrily cried the second. "I did, but I didn't mean to. Don't be angry," said the first quail, but the second quail was angry and said mean things.

Soon all the quails had taken sides in

this quarrel. When the fowler came that day, he flung his net over them, and this time instead of flying off with it, one side said, "Now, you lift the net," and the other side said, "Lift it yourself."

"You try to make us lift it all," said the quails on one side. "No, we don't!" said the others. "You begin and we will help." But neither side began.

So the quails quarreled, and while they were quarreling the fowler caught them all in his net. He took them to town and sold them for a good price.

The Bible Says

"If it be possible, as much as lieth in you, live peaceably with all men."

—Romans 12:18

43

Christopher Columbus

Hear a wonderful story. It is about a boy who lived long ago in a distant land. He grew up and became a great man. His name is now known all over the round world. It is Christopher Columbus.

His father was a poor man who lived with his wife and children in a beautiful city beside the sea.

Christopher was the oldest of four children. He had one sister. His two brothers were his best friends. In time of need, they gave him help and comfort. That was as it should be with brothers.

Little Christopher went to school and had lessons in reading, writing, grammar, and arithmetic. He also learned to draw.

Words to Watch For

distant	patient	purpose
explain	success	voyage

He studied geography as it was taught in those days. But he never saw a globe such as is in your schoolroom. Neither he nor his teacher knew that the earth is round. They thought it was flat, like a floor.

West of his home was the sea. He was told that west of that was another great body of water. This was called the Sea of Darkness. No one had ever crossed it. No one knew that beyond it lay our great land, America.

Men feared to sail out far on the Sea of Darkness. They thought they would come to strange monsters and boiling waves.

"And if we sail farther still," they said, "we shall come to the edge of the world and fall off."

So their ships never sailed far west. Instead, they kept near land and went east. There they found countries rich in spices, silks, and gold.

Little Christopher read travelers' tales about those distant lands. He listened to sailors' stories. Sometimes he went on board a ship ready to sail.

"Some day I will go to sea," he said. "Wherever other men sail, there I will go."

So Christopher went to a school where he studied many things which sailors need to know. He learned about sea roads and how to tell the way by the stars. He learned many things from books and from people.

But all these would have done him little good had he not learned more for himself. He learned to be brave and patient, and to carry out great plans with only a little money. This did not come all at once, you may be sure. It came little by little, day by day, year by year.

School days did not last long for Christopher. He became a sailor at fourteen. For many years he sailed on the sea.

He was in one sea battle which lasted all day long. At night both ships caught fire. The sailors jumped from the flames into the sea, and many were drowned.

But Columbus grabbed an oar. Sometimes swimming, sometimes floating, he reached the distant land. In later years he felt that God had saved him for a great purpose.

Years passed, and Columbus became a man. He lived in Portugal, a country beside the sea. There he married the daughter of a sea captain. To support his wife and his little son, he made maps and charts.

He liked to talk about the lands and people he had seen. He read travelers' tales and studied sailors' maps. He learned that some wise men believed the earth was round.

They said, "If a ship sails straight on, west or east, it will come back to the place from which it started."

But these men never went to find out if this were true. So most people kept on saying, "The earth is flat. It is flat like a floor."

Columbus thought much about the subject.

At last he said, "I do not think that the earth is flat. I am sure that it is round, like an orange. If it is, I can sail around it. I would like to do that."

People laughed. "The earth is not round," they said, "it is flat. Did not our fathers say so and their fathers before them? Who are you to call yourself wiser than they?"

"I am sure it is true," said Columbus. "If I can get ships and men, I will go to prove it."

But to get ships and men he must have money. He was only a poor sailor. What could he do?

He went to the king of Portugal and told his plan.

He said, "I am sure we can sail west and find a near road to the east. We can fill our ships with silks and spices. We can find lands of gold and gems. We can teach people about the one true God."

The king did a very unjust thing. He borrowed the charts and maps of Columbus and with them he sent out a ship of his own.

But a storm came up. The sailors were afraid of the great wild sea, and they came back.

Columbus was very angry. He would have no more to do with the unjust king.

"Now that your mother is dead," said he to his little son, "we will leave this land. Somewhere someone will be found to help carry out my plan."

He begged his way from city to city, from country to country. He was often sad and weary, but he never lost hope and faith. Nor was he too busy with his own plans to think of other people.

He went to see his old father and cared for his comfort. He talked over his plans with his brothers, and they did all they could to help. One of them went to England to ask aid.

Christopher Columbus himself started with his little son to Spain. Here some kind people gave him money and wrote a letter to the king and queen. Perhaps they could help him.

But the king and queen of Spain were busy with a war. They had no time to listen to a poor sailor's plan.

"I must wait," Columbus said.

Years passed. He made maps and charts for a living. Sometimes he followed the king to battle in the wild mountains. He talked to people about the plan which was a part of his life.

"He is a dreamer," some said.

Even the little children touched their foreheads as he passed. "He is a madman," they whispered.

At last Columbus had a chance to talk to the king and queen about his plan.

"It is a strange thing you want to do," said they. "We do not know what to think of it. We will hear what our wise men say."

They called together the most learned men of the land. The poor sailor explained his plan. Few listened; those few laughed him to scorn.

"Your words are silly and wicked," they said. "We cannot advise the king to waste ships and men on your plan."

So the king went off to fight and left Columbus again to wait.

Thus passed year after year. Columbus's gray hair became white. He was growing old. Seventeen years had gone in the effort to get aid, and still no help came.

Finally, the king and queen of Spain said that they would help. The queen even sold her jewels to get money for the trip.

Columbus was full of joy at his success, eager to sail westward.

But now a new trouble came. Sailors feared the unknown waters of the Sea of Darkness.

Where would he find men to sail with him?

The Pinzon brothers joined him. They had two little ships called the **Pinta** and **Nina**. Columbus at last got a third ship, the **Santa Maria**.

On a summer day in 1492, the three little ships sailed from Spain. People on shore were sobbing and crying.

"Why will you go to danger and to death?" they cried to their friends on board.

The hearts of the sailors failed them. They were leaving behind friends, family, and life itself. Before them was the danger and the terror of unknown seas. They cried aloud like children.

Columbus tried to comfort them. He told them of lands of gold and gems far to the west.

On they sailed. An east wind pushed them forward. For days and days they saw nothing but sea and sky. The sailors began to complain.

"We do not believe your foolish tale that the earth is round," they said. "This east wind is taking us away from home. How can we ever sail back against it?" Then the wind sank and there came a calm.

"Must we lie here on this still, hot sea and die?" they asked.

One day two or three sailors stood talking on the deck of Columbus's ship. Man after man joined them.

"We have followed him on this unknown sea," said one. "Shall we go on and on until it is too late to turn back? Shall we follow him and die? Or shall we think of our own safety and go home?"

"Who is this Columbus that we should obey him?" asked another. "He is a stranger, without friends in Spain. The wise men laughed at his plan. If we go back, people will say that we did well. Let us tell him we will go home."

"Yes," said a third man, "and if he will not go back, let us throw him in the sea. We can say he was watching the stars and fell overboard."

Columbus was both wise and brave. To the men that were frightened, he said, "Be of good cheer, my friends. We are as safe today as when we set sail. Look at the seaweed, the birds, the driftwood—all signs of land. Soon we shall reach the land we seek and go safely home. Sail on!"

And sure enough, there soon rose a cry of "Land! land!" To the west there seemed to be a far-off shore. But when morning came, they saw that it was only a cloud.

At last the men said, "We will not go on."

"I will not turn back," said Columbus. "I sailed on this western sea to find land. With the help of God, I will go on till I succeed."

On they sailed, always looking for land. One night Columbus saw far to the west a light which rose and fell. It looked like a torch in the hand of a man moving back and forth.

"Did I indeed see it?" Columbus asked himself, "or do I just imagine it?"

He called a sailor. "Look!—there to the west. Do you see a light?"

"Yes," said the sailor, "I see it. A light! A light! Land is near!"

Few eyes were closed that night. Early in the morning, they did indeed see land.

The sailors were full of eager questions. "Is it some country we have seen before? Is it an unknown land? Shall we find silks and spices, gold and gems? Or is it a land of dangers and strange monsters?"

The sun rose. In the light of the October morning, the men could see a beautiful island. Its coast was green with groves and forests. Red-brown people ran about the shore.

Columbus had come to the end of his voyage. He had sailed west and found land. But it was not the eastern country he had expected to reach. He had not found spices and gold and gems. He had found something better than gold. He had sailed west and found a new world. He had discovered America.

The Fisherman and His Wife

Once upon a time a fisherman and his wife lived in a little old hut close by the sea. Every day the fisherman went fishing in his boat.

One day while he was out fishing, the fisherman felt a great tug on his line. What-

Words to Watch For

gigantic	amazement	enchanted
vanish	dainty	appear
discontented	elegant	doubtfully

ever was on his line dragged the boat out into the deep water.

The fisherman pulled with all his might. At last he was able to bring in the gigantic fish that was on his hook.

To the fisherman's amazement, the fish spoke. "Please let me go," it said. "I am not a real fish, you know. I am an enchanted prince."

"Oh!" said the fisherman, very much surprised. "Swim away, fish. Swim away fast. I do not want to have anything to do with a fish that can talk."

He put the huge fish back into the water, and it swam down toward the bottom of the sea and vanished.

When the fisherman went home to his wife in the little hut, he told her about the fish that could talk.

"Did you not ask him for anything?" asked the wife.

"No, indeed," said the fisherman. "What should I have asked for?"

"It would be fine," said the wife, "if we had a dainty little cottage, instead of this dingy hut. Do go back and ask the fish to give us a dainty little cottage."

The fisherman did not like to go, but he went back to the seashore. When he came to the water, it appeared all yellow and green.

He stood at the water's edge, and looking down, said,

"O Man of the Sea,

Come listen to me!

My wife Ilsabil

Will have her own will,

And hath sent me to beg

A boon of thee."

The fish came swimming to him, and asked, "What does she want?"

"A cottage," said the fisherman. "She says she is tired of living in a little hut."

"You can go home," said the fish. "She is in the cottage already."

So the fisherman went home, and there was his wife at the door of a dainty little cottage.

"Come in! Come in!" she said. "Is not this better than the hut?"

There was a pretty living room, a

bedroom, and a kitchen, and there was a little garden behind the cottage. In the garden grew cucumbers, peas, and all kinds of vegetables.

"O **Wife,** how happy we shall be!" said the fisherman.

Everything went happily for a week or two, and then the wife became discontented again. "Husband, I am tired of this cottage," she said. "Ask the fish to give us an elegant castle."

"I don't like to ask him," said the fisherman doubtfully. "It may make him very angry."

"Oh, no!" said the wife. "You will find that he will do it very willingly."

So the fisherman went to the sea. The water was blue and gloomy, but he went close to the edge, and said,

"O Man of the Sea,

Come listen to me!

My wife Ilsabil

Will have her own will,

And hath sent me to beg

A boon of thee."

"What does she want now?" asked the fish.

"Well," said the fisherman, "she is tired of the cottage. She wants an elegant castle."

"Go home," said the fish. "You will find

her standing at the gate of an elegant castle."

Away went the fisherman, and there was his wife standing at the gate of an elegant castle.

"See, Husband!" she said. "Is not this much better than the little cottage?"

They went into the castle, and there were

servants, and many rooms with expensive golden chairs and tables. Behind the castle was a garden, and around it was a beautiful park.

"Now we shall be happy," said the fisherman.

Early the next morning, when the fisherman awoke, his wife said, "Husband, go to the fish and tell him to make me king of all the land."

"Wife! Wife!" said the fisherman. "You cannot be king. The fish cannot make you king."

"Yes, he can," said the wife. "Go and ask him."

So, very sadly, the fisherman returned to the sea.

The water was dark gray, and the waves were white with foam.

He stood at the edge of the water and cried,

"O Man of the Sea,

Come listen to me!

My wife Ilsabil

Will have her own will,

And hath sent me to beg

A boon of thee."

"Well!" said the fish. "What now?"

"Alas!" said the fisherman. "My wife wants to be king."

"Go home," said the fish. "She is king already."

So the fisherman went home, and there was his wife sitting on a throne of gold and silver.

"Well, Wife," said the fisherman, "are you king?"

"Yes," said she, "I am king."

"What a fine thing it is to be king!" said the fisherman. "You will never have anything more to wish for as long as you live."

"I don't know about that," said the wife.

The next day Dame Ilsabil had grown tired of being king. So she said to the fisherman, "Husband, go to the fish, and tell him to make me Lord of the Sun and the Moon."

"Wife! Wife!" said the fisherman. "The fish cannot make you Lord of the Sun and the Moon."

But Dame Ilsabil grew very angry, and at last the fisherman went.

When he came to the sea, the wind was blowing, the waves were raging, and the fisherman grew afraid. Nevertheless, he went down to the water's edge and said,

"O Man of the Sea,
Come listen to me!
My wife Ilsabil
Will have her own will,
And hath sent me to beg
A boon of thee."

"What is it now?" asked the fish.

"My wife wants to be Lord of the Sun and the Moon," said the fisherman.

"Go home," said the fish, "to your little old hut again."

And there they have lived to this day.

What Do You Think?

1. Do you think that this is a true story? Why not?
2. Which person would you rather have for a friend— the fisherman or his wife?
3. Which person do you think was happier— the fisherman or his wife? Why?
4. What do you think was wrong with Dame Ilsabil?
5. If you could meet Dame Ilsabil, what would you tell her?

The Bible Says

"Let your conversation be without covetousness; and be content with such things as ye have: for he hath said, I will never leave thee, nor forsake thee."

—*Hebrews 13:5*

The Banyan Deer

There was once a deer the color of gold. His eyes were like round jewels, his horns were white as silver, his mouth was red like a flower, his hoofs were bright and hard. He had a large body and a fine tail.

He lived in a forest, and was the king of a herd of five hundred banyan. Nearby lived another herd of deer, called the monkey deer. They, too, had a king.

The prince of that country was fond of

hunting the deer and eating deer meat. He did not like to go alone, so he called the people of his town to go with him, day after day.

The townspeople did not like this, for while they were gone, no one did their work. So they decided to make a park and drive the deer into it. Then the prince could go into the park and hunt, and they could go on with their daily work.

They made a park, planted grass in it, and provided water for the deer. Then they built a fence all around it and drove the deer into it.

They shut the gate and went to the prince to tell him that in the park nearby he could find all the deer he wanted.

The prince went at once to look at the deer. First he saw there the two deer kings, and granted them their lives. Then he looked at their great herds.

Some days the prince would go to hunt the deer; sometimes his cook would go. As soon as any of the deer saw them they would shake with fear and run. But when they had been hit once or twice, they would drop down dead.

The King of the Banyan Deer sent for the King of the Monkey Deer and said, "Friend, many of the deer are being killed. Many are wounded besides those who are killed. After this suppose one from my herd goes up to be killed one day, and the next day let one from your herd go up. Fewer deer will be lost this way."

The monkey deer agreed. Each day the deer whose turn it was would go and lie down, placing its head on the block. The cook would come and carry off the one he found lying there.

One day the lot fell to a mother deer who had a young baby. She went to her king and said, "O King of the Monkey Deer, let the turn pass me by until my baby is old enough to get along without me. Then I will go and put my head on the block."

But the king did not help her. He told her that if the lot had fallen to her she must die.

Then she went to the King of the Banyan Deer and asked him to save her.

"Go back to your herd. I will go in your place," said he.

The next day the cook found the King of the Banyan Deer lying with his head on the block. The cook went to the prince, who came himself to find out about this.

"King of the Banyan Deer, did I not grant you your life? Why are you lying here?"

"O great Prince!" said the King of the Banyan Deer, "a mother came with her young baby and told me that the lot had fallen to her. I could not ask anyone else to take her place, so I came myself."

"King of the Banyan Deer! I never saw such kindness and mercy. Rise up. I grant your life and hers. Nor will I hunt any more of the deer in either park or forest."

Something to Do

Describe the King of the Banyan Deer. What did he look like? Was he a good thinker? How do you know? Was he kind? How do you know?

The Bible Says

"Greater love hath no man than this, that a man lay down his life for his friends."

—*John 15:13*

The Story of Wylie

This is a story about a dog, a slim, silky-haired, sharp-eared little dog, the prettiest thing you can imagine. Her name was Wylie, and she lived in Scotland, far up on the hills. She helped her master take care of his sheep.

You can't think how clever she was! She watched over the sheep and the little lambs like a soldier, and never let anything hurt them. She drove them out to pasture when it was time, and brought them safely home when it was time for that. When the silly sheep got frightened and ran this way and that, hurting themselves and getting lost, Wylie knew exactly what to do. Round on one side she would run, barking and scolding, driving them back. Then round on the other, barking and scolding, driving them back, till they were all bunched together in front of the right gate. Then she drove them through as neatly as any person. She loved her work, and was a wonderfully fine sheep dog.

At last her master grew too old to stay alone on the hills, and so he gave Wylie to two kind young men who lived in the nearest town. He knew they would be good to her. They grew very fond of her, because she was so gentle and handsome and well-behaved.

So now Wylie lived in the city where there were no sheep farms. There were only streets and houses, and she did not have to do any work at all—she was just a pet dog. She seemed very happy, and she was always good.

But after a while, the family noticed something odd, something very strange indeed, about their pet. Every single Tuesday night, about nine o'clock, Wylie disappeared. They would look for her, and call her, but she was gone. And she would be gone all night. But every Wednesday morning, there she was at the door, waiting to be let in. Her silky coat was all sweaty and muddy and her feet heavy with weariness. But her bright eyes looked up at her masters as if she were trying to explain where she had been.

Week after week the same thing happened. Nobody could imagine where Wylie went every Tuesday night. They tried to follow her to find out, but she always slipped away. They tried to shut her in, but she always found a way out. It grew to be a real mystery. Where in the world did Wylie go?

You never could guess, so I am going to tell you.

In the city near the town where the kind young men lived was a big market. Every sort of thing was sold there, even live cows and sheep and hens. On Tuesday nights, the farmers used to come down from the hills with their sheep to sell. They drove them through the city streets into the pens, ready to sell on Wednesday morning.

The sheep weren't used to the city noises and sights. They always grew afraid and wild, and gave the farmers and the sheep dogs a great deal of trouble. They broke away and ran about, getting in everybody's way.

But just as the trouble was at its worst, about sunrise the farmer would see a little silky, sharp-eared dog come trotting all alone down the road, into the midst of them.

And then!

In and out the little dog ran like the wind, round and about, always in the right place, driving—coaxing—pushing—making the sheep mind like a good schoolteacher, and never frightening them, till they were all safely in! All the other dogs together could not do as much as the little strange dog. She was a perfect wonder. And no one knew whose dog she was or where she came from. The farmers began to watch for her every week, and they called her "the wee fell yin," which is Scotch for "the little terror." They used to say when they saw her coming, "There's the wee fell yin! Now we'll get them in."

Every farmer would have liked to keep her, but she let no one catch her. As soon as her work was done, she was off and away like a fairy dog, no one knew where. Week after week this happened, and nobody knew who the little strange dog was.

But one day Wylie went to walk with her two masters, and they happened to meet some sheep-farmers. The sheep-farmers stopped short and stared at Wylie, and then they cried out, "Why, that's the dog! That's the wee fell yin!" And so it was. The little strange dog who helped with the sheep was Wylie.

Her masters, of course, didn't know what the farmers meant, till they were told all about what I have been telling you. But when they heard about the **pretty,** strange dog who came to market all alone, they knew at last where Wylie went every Tuesday night. And they loved her better than ever.

Wasn't it wise of the little dog to go and work for other people when her own work was taken away? I guess she knew that the best people and the best dogs always work hard at something. Anyway, she did that same thing as long as she lived, and she was always just as gentle and silky-haired and loving as at first.

Do You Remember?
1. What was Wylie's job on the farm?
2. Why did Wylie move to town?
3. What was the mystery about Wylie?
4. What did Wylie's new masters find out about her?

Five Peas in a Pod

There were once five peas in one pod. They were green and the pod was green, so they believed that the whole world must be green also. The pod grew, and the peas grew, sitting all in a row. The sun shone without and warmed the pod, and the rain made it clear and transparent. As the peas grew bigger and bigger, they began to think.

"Are we to sit here forever?" asked one.

Words to Watch For

transparent	immediately	industrious
delicate	patient	amuse

"We shall become hard by sitting so long. It seems to me there must be something outside, and I feel sure of it."

Weeks went by. The peas became yellow, and the pod became yellow.

"All the world is turning yellow, I suppose," said they.

Suddenly they felt a pull at the shell. It was torn off and held in human hands, then slipped into the pocket of a jacket in company with other pods.

"Now we shall soon be opened," said one. "I wonder what shall become of us?"

"I should like to know which of us will travel farthest," said the smallest of the five. "We shall soon see now."

"What is to happen, will happen," said the largest pea.

"Crack!" went the shell as it burst, and the five peas rolled out into the bright sunshine. There they lay in a child's hand. A little boy was holding them tightly. "These will be fine peas for my peashooter," he said. Immediately he put one in and shot it out.

"Now I am flying out into the wide world," said the pea. "Catch me if you can." And he was gone in a moment.

"I," said the second, "intend to fly straight to the sun. That is a shell that lets itself be seen, and it will suit me exactly."

"We will go to sleep wherever we find ourselves," said the next two.

"What is to happen, will happen," exclaimed the last, as he was shot out of the peashooter. As he spoke, he flew up against an old board under a cottage window and fell into a little crack.

"What is to happen, will happen," said he to himself.

Within the little cottage lived a poor woman. She went out every day to clean stoves, chop wood into small pieces, and

perform other hard tasks, for she was strong and industrious. Yet she remained always poor, and at home in the cottage lay her only daughter, who was very delicate and weak. For a whole year she had been sick in bed, and it seemed as if she could neither live nor die. Quietly and patiently she lay there all day long, while her mother was at work.

Spring came, and one morning early the sun shone brightly through the little window and threw its rays over the floor of the room.

Just as the mother was going to her work, the sick girl fixed her gaze on the lowest pane of the window.

"Mother," she exclaimed, "what can that little green thing be that peeps in at the window? It is moving in the wind."

The mother stepped to the window and half opened it. "Oh!" she said, "there is a little pea here. It has taken root and is putting out its green leaves. How could it have gotten into this crack? Well, now, here is a little garden for you to amuse yourself with."

The mother pushed the bed of the sick girl nearer to the window so she might see the budding plant. Then she went out to her work.

"Mother, I believe I shall get well," said the sick girl in the evening. "The sun has shone in here so bright and warm today, and the little pea is thriving so well. I shall get on better, too, and go out into the warm sunshine again."

"God grant it!" said the mother, but she did not believe it would be so. She propped up with a little stick the green plant which had given her child such pleasant hopes of life. She did not want it to be broken by the winds. She tied the piece of string to the windowsill and to the upper part of the frame so that the pea tendrils might twine round it when it shot up. And it did shoot up; indeed, the little girl could almost see it grow from day to day.

"Look, here is a flower coming," said the old woman one morning. Now at last she began to hope that her little sick daughter might really recover. The child had seemed more cheerful. During the last few days she had raised herself in bed in the morning to look with sparkling eyes at her little garden, which contained only a single pea plant.

A week later the girl sat up a whole hour for the first time, feeling quite happy by the open window in the warm sunshine. Outside grew the little plant, and on it a pink pea blossom was in full bloom. The little maiden bent down and gently kissed the delicate leaves.

"Our heavenly Father Himself has planted the pea and made it grow, to bring joy to you and hope to me, my child," said

the happy mother. She smiled at the flower as if it had been an angel from God.

But what became of the other peas? Why, the one who flew out into the wide world and said, "Catch me if you can," fell into a gutter and ended his travels in the crop of a pigeon. The two lazy ones were also eaten by pigeons, so they were at least of some use. But the fourth, who wanted to reach the sun, fell into a sink and lay there in the dirty water for days and weeks, till he had swelled to a great size.

But as the young maiden stood at the open cottage window, with sparkling eyes and the rosy hue of health on her cheeks, she folded her thin hands over the pea blossom, and thanked God for what He had done.

The Cowardly Lion

Dorothy, the Scarecrow, the Tin Man and the little dog, Toto, were walking through a forest looking for the Wizard of Oz. Suddenly, a terrible roar sounded in their ears, and the next moment a great Lion bounded into the road. With one blow of his paw he sent the Scarecrow spinning over and over to the edge of the road, and then he struck at the Tin Woodman with his sharp claws. But, to the Lion's surprise, he could make no impression on the tin, although the Woodman fell over in the road and lay still.

Little Toto, now that he had an enemy

Words to Watch For

impression	continue	disease
astonished	retort	coward

to face, ran barking toward the Lion, and the
great beast had opened his mouth to bite
the dog, when Dorothy, fearing Toto would
be killed, and heedless of danger, rushed
forward and slapped the Lion upon his nose
as hard as she could, while she cried out,

"Don't you dare bite Toto! You ought to be ashamed of yourself, a big beast like you, to bite a poor little dog!"

"I didn't bite him," said the Lion, as he rubbed his nose with his paw, where Dorothy had hit it.

"No, but you tried to," she retorted. "You are nothing but a big coward."

"I know it," said the Lion, hanging his head in shame. "I've always known it. But how can I help it?"

"I don't know, I'm sure," she replied. "To think of your striking a stuffed man, like the poor Scarecrow!"

"Oh, is he stuffed?" asked the Lion, in surprise, as he watched her pick up the Scarecrow and set him upon his feet, while she patted him into shape again.

"Of course he's stuffed," said Dorothy, who was still angry.

"That's why he went over so easily,"

remarked the Lion. "It astonished me to see him whirl around so. Is the other one stuffed also?"

"No," said Dorothy, "he's made of tin." And she helped the Woodman up again.

"That's why he nearly blunted my claws," said the Lion. "When they scratched against the tin it made a cold shiver run down my back. What is the little animal you are so tender of?"

"He is my dog, Toto," answered the girl.

"Is he made of tin, or is he stuffed?" asked the Lion.

"Neither one. He's a-a-a meat dog," said Dorothy.

"Oh. He's a curious animal, and seems remarkably small, now that I look at him. No one would think of biting such a little thing except a coward like me," continued the Lion sadly.

"What makes you a coward?" Dorothy

asked, looking at the great beast in wonder.

"It's a mystery," replied the Lion. "I suppose I was born that way. All the other animals in the forest naturally expect me to be brave, for the Lion is everywhere thought to be the King of Beasts. I learned that if I roared very loudly, every living thing was frightened and got out of my way. Whenever I've met a man, I've been awfully scared. But I just roared at him, and he has always run away as fast as he could go. If the elephants and the tigers and the bears had ever tried to fight me, I should have run myself—I'm such a coward. But just as soon as they hear me roar, they all try to get away from me, and of course I let them go."

"But that isn't right. The King of Beasts shouldn't be a coward," said the Scarecrow.

"I know it," returned the Lion, wiping a tear from his eye with the tip of his tail. "It is my great sorrow, and makes my life very unhappy. But whenever there is danger, my heart begins to beat fast."

"Perhaps you have heart disease," said the Tin Woodman.

"It may be," said the Lion.

"No," declared Dorothy, "that doesn't 'splain it. I guess it's lion nature, because it's human nature. Out West in Kansas, where I live, they always say that the cowboy that roars the loudest and claims he's the baddest man, is sure to be the biggest coward of all."

A Little Dutch Hero

Holland is a little country of Europe where the ground is lower than the level of the sea, instead of higher as it is in our country. Long ago the Hollanders saw that the water would run in and cover the land and the houses if they did not do something to keep it out. So they built great thick walls around their country to shut out the sea. Those walls, which are called "dikes," protect the good crops, the houses, and even the people.

Once a little boy named Hans lived in that country. One day Hans took his little brother out by the dike to play. They went a long way off where there were no houses, only flowers and green fields. Hans climbed up on the high dike and sat down; the little brother was playing at the foot of the bank.

Suddenly the little brother called out, "Oh, what a funny little hole. It bubbles."

"Hole? Where?" said Hans.

"Here in the bank," said the little brother. "Water's in it."

"What!" said Hans, and he slid down as fast as he could to where his brother was playing.

There was the tiniest hole in the bank—just an airhole. A drop of water bubbled slowly through.

"It is a hole in the dike!" cried Hans. "What shall we do?" He looked all around; not a person or a house was in sight. He looked at the hole. He knew that the water would soon break a great gap. The town was far away—if they ran for help it would be too late; what should he do?

Suddenly a thought came to Hans. He stuck his little forefinger right into the hole, where it fit tightly; and he said to his little brother:

"Run fast! Go to the town and tell the

men there's a hole in the dike. Tell them I will keep it stopped till they get here."

The brother knew by Hans's face that something very serious was wrong, and he started off as fast as he could run. Hans, kneeling with his finger in the hole, watched him grow smaller and smaller as he got farther and farther away, until he was only a speck; then he was out of sight. Hans was all alone, squatted on the ground with his finger right in the bank. He could hear the water, slap, slap, slapping on the stones. It seemed very near.

By and by, his hand began to feel numb. He rubbed it with the other hand; but it got colder and more numb, colder and more numb, every minute. He looked to see if the men were coming; the road was bare as far as he could see. Then the cold began creeping, creeping, up his arm; first his wrist, then his arm to the elbow, then his arm to the shoulder; how cold it was!

Soon it began to ache. Ugly little cramp-pains streamed up his finger, up his palm, up his arm, till it ached way into his shoulder, and down the back of his neck. It seemed hours since the little brother had gone away. He felt very lonely, and the hurt in his arm grew and grew. He watched the road intently, but no one came in sight. Then he leaned his head against the dike to rest his shoulder.

As his ear touched the dike, he heard the voice of the great sea, murmuring. The sound seemed to say, "I am the great sea.

No one can stand against me. What are you, a little child, that you try to keep me out? Beware! Beware!"

Hans's heart beat in heavy knocks. Would they never come? He was frightened. And the water went on beating at the wall, and murmuring, "I will come through, I will come through, I will get you. I will get you, run—run—before I come through!"

Hans started to pull out his finger; he was so frightened that he felt as if he must run forever. But that minute he remembered how much depended on him; if he pulled out his finger, the water would surely make the hole bigger, and at last break down the dike, and the sea would come in on all the land and houses. He set his teeth and stuck his finger in tighter than ever.

"You shall not come through!" he whispered. "I will not run!"

Just then he heard a far-off shout. Far

in the distance he saw something on the road. The men were coming! At last, they were coming. They came nearer. He could make out his own father and the neighbors. They had pickaxes and shovels. They were running, and as they ran they shouted, "We're coming; take heart, we're coming!"

The next minute they were there. When they saw Hans with his pale face and his hand tight in the dike, they gave a great cheer—just as people do for soldiers back from war. They lifted him up and rubbed his aching arm with gentle hands. They told him that he was a real hero, and that he had saved the town.

When the men had mended the dike, they marched home carrying Hans high on their shoulders, because he was a hero. Even to this day the people of that town tell the story of how a little boy saved the dike.

Clara Barton

"Rock-a-bye," sang a little girl, as she held a struggling kitten tightly against her and rocked it back and forth. The kitten mewed, but Clara only hugged it tighter and continued with her songs.

She had never had a doll. Her parents

Words to Watch For

gratitude   enable   carriages

thought it very foolish for children to have toys. She had, instead, many pets of all kinds—kittens, dogs, ducks, chickens, colts, and calves. She lived on a farm and could spend her playtime in loving them and playing with them. There was not a horse that she could not ride, even though she had taken many a tumble in learning to do so.

Clara had been born on Christmas day, and was the youngest of five children. She had two big brothers and two sisters. Three of them were teachers. They took great delight in teaching the baby of the family. Before she was three years old, she could read. Soon after this her big brother took her to school with him, carrying her most of the way on his shoulder. She learned very rapidly, not only reading, but also spelling, arithmetic, and geography.

When she was still a little girl, her father moved to a large farm. On this place were three barns. What fun she had there! She soon learned to walk along the big beams that went from one side to the other above the hay. Often, halfway across a beam, she would pretend that she was a bird and go flying to the soft hay beneath.

Through the meadows ran a deep river. A short way up this river was a mill. Here she often played alone. Playing so much by herself made her very quiet when she was with others, but she grew strong and rosy.

One day when she was eleven years old, her brother fell from the top of a barn and was hurt. It was thought that he would not live. He wanted Clara to stay beside him, and she proved to be such a good nurse that the doctor would allow no one else to care for him. It was two years before he was well. Even though Clara missed school during this time, she was ahead of the other pupils of her own age when she went back.

When Clara Barton was older, she taught school. The children loved her. At recess time, she went out and played games with them. She taught for sixteen years, and then she went to work for the government in Washington. While she was there, war broke out between the North and the South. Miss Barton had always liked to take care of sick people, so she offered her services as a nurse.

The people in the North heard of the work she was doing, and they began to send her food, medicine, and all kinds of supplies for the poor sick soldiers. Since there were few dishes, she used whatever she could get to serve the sick—cans, jars, and jelly glasses. The men drank from these with tears of gratitude in their eyes. The government gave her teams and wagons to enable her to carry the supplies with her.

Whenever there was a battle, she would go to the place and do what she could for the wounded. She never was afraid on a battle-field. She went through all kinds of dangers bravely, never thinking of possible danger to herself. Many other brave men and women were glad to help her. As long as the war lasted, through winter and summer, in rain and sunshine, she lived outdoors in tents.

Once a man who was slowly dying wished he had a custard pie. Clara, who had been taught by her mother to cook, made him one. The sick man smiled happily when he saw it. It was a beautiful pie, a golden brown with tiny little crinkles all around the edge. It is said that she had to milk a

cow in a field nearby to get the milk for it. It is certain that she could milk, for there was very little that Clara had not learned how to do when she lived on the farm.

After the war was over, many men were missing. President Lincoln asked her to help him find out what had become of them. She worked hard at this, and found out what had become of many of the men.

Then, tired and sick, she went to Europe. She lived in Switzerland, in the beautiful mountains called the Alps.

One day she was surprised to see grand carriages drive up. In them were a king's daughter and other royal men and women. They had come to welcome Clara Barton. They had heard of what she had done in America during the war. It had made her famous all over the world.

Later when war broke out in France, the leaders of the Red Cross Society there asked her to help them. Although she was not fully well, she again went to work. The Red Cross Society was a new organization. It had been formed to help the wounded in times of war. Anyone wearing a Red Cross band upon his or her arm, or carrying a white flag with the red cross upon it, was never fired upon. These nurses could care for friend or enemy alike. Before she went home, France gave Miss Barton a cross of honor. She had been very brave, and they were grateful for what she had done for them.

When she got home, Clara Barton wanted America to have a Red Cross society, too. She talked to the President about it. Six years afterwards, the first American Red Cross Society was formed, and Clara Barton was its first president.

She thought the American Red Cross should serve not only in war time, but during peace as well. When there was sickness or trouble of any kind, or when she heard of countries not having enough food, Clara went to work to get people to give money to help those needing it. She went on helping people through her whole lifetime. She was always known as a friend to everyone in trouble.

Do You Remember?

1. What was Clara Barton like when she was a girl?
2. What was she like when she was a teacher?
3. What was she like when she was a nurse?

The Violet

A violet by a mossy stone,
Half hidden from the eye,
Fair as a star, when only one
Is shining in the sky.

—*William Wordsworth*

The Cock,
the Mouse,
and the Little Red Hen

Once upon a time there was a hill, and on the hill there was a pretty little house.

It had one little door and four little windows. In this house lived a cock and a mouse and a little red hen.

On another hill not far away there was another house. It had a door that wouldn't shut, and it had two broken windows. In this house there lived a bad old fox and four bad little foxes.

One morning these four bad little foxes came to the bad old fox and said, "Oh, Father, we are hungry!"

"We had nothing to eat yesterday," said the first little fox.

"And not much the day before," said the second.

"And only half a chicken the day before that," said the third.

"And only two little ducks the day before that," said the fourth.

The bad old fox shook his head for a long time. He was thinking.

At last he said, "On the hill over there I see a house. In that house lives a cock."

"And a mouse!" said two little foxes.

"And a hen!" said the other two.

"They are all fat," said the bad old fox. "I will take my big bag and I will go up that

hill and into that house. I will put the cock, the mouse, and the little red hen into my bag and bring them home."

"I'll make a fire to cook the cock," said the first little fox.

"I'll put on the pot to cook the hen," said the second.

"I'll get the pan to cook the mouse," said the third.

"And I'll have the biggest helping when they are all cooked," said the fourth, who was very greedy.

So the little foxes jumped for joy, and the bad old fox went to get his bag.

But what were the cock and the mouse and the little red hen doing all this time?

Well, the cock and the mouse had got out of bed on the wrong side that morning. The cock said the weather was too hot, and the mouse said it was too cold.

They came downstairs where the good

little red hen was at work.

"Who will make the fire?" she asked.

"I will not," said the cock.

"I will not," said the mouse.

"Then I'll do it myself," said the little red hen.

So she made the fire.

"Now who will go for some water?" she asked.

"I will not," said the cock.

"I will not," said the mouse.

"Then I'll do it myself," said the little red hen.

So off she ran for the water.

"Now who will cook the breakfast?" she asked.

"I will not," said the cock.

"I will not," said the mouse.

"Then I'll do it myself," said the little red hen.

So she cooked the breakfast and they all ate it.

After breakfast the little red hen said, "Now who will help me make the beds?"

The cock said, "I will not."

The mouse said, "I will not."

"Then I'll do it myself," said the little red hen.

So she went to make the beds.

The cross cock and the lazy mouse sat

down by the fire, and soon they fell fast asleep.

Now the bad old fox had come up the hill and into the garden. If the cock and the mouse had not been asleep, they would have seen his bright eyes looking in at the window.

"Rat-tat-tat! Rat-tat-tat!" The fox knocked at the door.

"Who can that be?" said the mouse, half opening his eyes.

"Go and look, if you want to know," said the cross cock.

"It may be the mailman," thought the mouse, "and he may have a letter for me."

So he went to the door and opened it.

In jumped the bad old fox!

"Oh! oh! oh!" squeaked the mouse.

"Cock-a-doodle-doo!" screamed the cock.

The fox laughed. "Ha, ha, ha!"

He caught the little mouse by the tail and put him into the bag. Then he caught the cock by the neck and put him into the bag.

The little red hen came running down-stairs to see what all the noise was about. The fox caught her and put her into the bag with the others.

Then he threw the bag over his back, and off he went down the hill.

It was a warm day, and soon Mr. Fox's bag began to feel heavy. So he threw the bag on the ground and lay down under a tree to rest. He fell fast asleep and began to snore.

As soon as the little red hen heard the fox snoring, she took out her scissors and cut a hole in the bag, just big enough for the mouse to creep through.

"Quick!" she said to the mouse. "Run as fast as you can, and bring back a stone to put in your place."

The mouse ran out and got a stone.

"Put it in," said the little red hen.

The mouse put the stone into the bag.

Then the little red hen cut the hole till it was big enough for the cock to get through.

"Quick!" she said. "Run and get a stone to put in your place."

The cock flew out. He got a stone and put it into the bag.

Then the little red hen came out. She got a stone and put it into the bag. Then she sewed up the hole in the bag.

The cock and the mouse and the little red

hen ran home as fast as their legs could carry them.

At last the bad old fox woke up.

"Dear me," he said, rubbing his eyes. "It is getting late. I must go home."

So he took up his bag and went on down the hill. He came to the river at the foot of the hill.

Splash! In went one foot. Splash! In went the other foot. The stones in the bag were so heavy that at the next step Mr. Fox fell down in the river.

The four bad little foxes waited and waited for their father to come home, but he never came.

So the first little fox never cooked the cock; the second little fox never cooked the hen; the third little fox never cooked the mouse; and the fourth little fox never got any helping at all.

The cock and the mouse had learned not

to be cross or lazy. They made the fire and went for the water. They cooked the breakfast and helped the little red hen do all the work.

And for all I know they are still happily living in the pretty little house on the hill.

Do You Know?

1. Why did the cock and the mouse always say, "I will not"?
2. Why did the cock and the mouse not see the fox come over the hill?
3. Why did the fox throw the bag on the ground?
4. Why did the cock and the mouse begin to work?
5. Why are the cock, the mouse, and the little red hen happy now?

The Mountain
and the Squirrel

The Mountain and the Squirrel
Had a quarrel,
The former called the latter
"Little Prig."

Bun replied:
"You are doubtless very big!
But all sorts of things and weather
Must be taken in together
To make up a year;
And a sphere;
And I think it no disgrace
To occupy my place.

If I'm not so large as you,

You're not so small as I,

And not half so spry;

I'll not deny you make

A very pretty squirrel track.

Talents differ; all is well and wisely put;

If I cannot carry forests on my back,

Neither can you crack a nut."

—*Ralph Waldo Emerson*

The Fox and the Grapes

It was a sultry day, and the fox was almost famished with hunger and thirst. He was just saying to himself that anything would be acceptable, when, looking up, he spied some great clusters of ripe, black grapes hanging from a vine.

"What luck!" he said. "If only they weren't quite so high, I should be sure of a fine feast! I wonder if I can get them? I can think of nothing that would refresh me more."

Jumping into the air is not the easiest thing in the world for a fox to do, but he gave a great spring and nearly reached the lowest clusters.

"I'll do better next time," he said.

Words to Watch For

sultry   famished   acceptable

Sultry means very hot.

He tried again and again, but did not succeed. Finding, at last, that he was losing his strength, and that he had little chance of getting the grapes, he walked off slowly, grumbling, "The grapes are sour, and not at all fit for my eating. I'll leave them to the greedy birds. They eat anything."